Contents

C000007333

The letter **s**

▶ Say the letter sound.

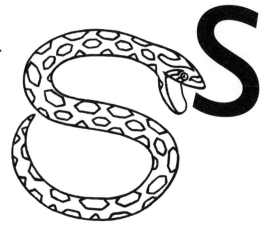

▶ Point to each letter and say the sound.

s   s   s

▶ Join the letter below to the things that begin with this sound.

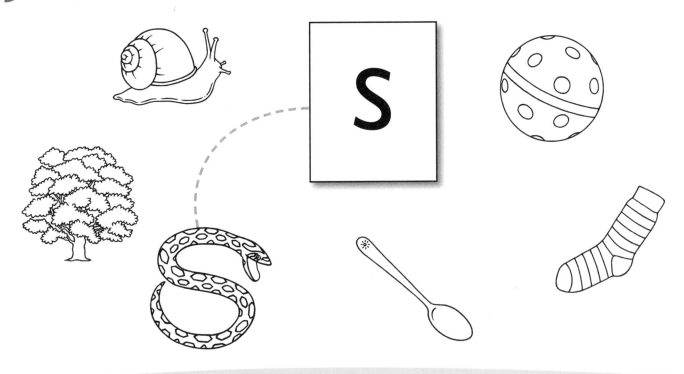

FOCUS ● recognise the letter **s** and say the sound that it represents

● select words that start with that sound

Notes for teachers

Sound Phonics supports the teaching and learning of phonics. It can be used in school or at home, providing children with opportunities to apply and practise their developing phonic knowledge and skills. Ten graded activity books are supported by a **Teacher's Guide** and **Teacher's Resource Book**, as well as **Rhymes for Reading** – a photocopiable collection of phonically decodable rhymes for Phases Two to Four. The series follows the same basic structure as the systematic phonics resource *Letters and Sounds* (© Crown copyright 2007) and can also be used with other incremental phonics programmes.

Encouraging a multi-sensory approach

Hearing and speaking

The **Sound Phonics** activities are most effective if the child works through them with an adult. This gives the child the opportunity to say and listen to the letter sounds, practising phonic skills orally as well as on the page.

Touch, sight and movement

Many of the activities can be repeated using solid plastic letters: handling these and feeling their shape can help children to recognise and remember the letters. The segmenting and blending activities can also be recreated using magnetic letters on a fridge door or in a tin tray.

Tracing letter shapes helps children to remember the letters and how to form them correctly. At this stage, many children will still be developing the physical skills necessary to correctly form letters in pencil. In this book they are asked to point to the relevant letters and occasionally to trace their outlines with one finger (see pages 13, 21 and 31). They should also be encouraged to form the letter shapes in the air, in sand or using a paintbrush.

In school, children are helped to remember letter shapes, how they are formed and the sounds they represent, using pictures, rhymes and hand movements. All these can be referred to as they work through the appropriate page of this book.

Focus statements

The 'Focus' notes at the foot of each page summarise the teaching objectives for that page, expressed simply so that any adult working with the child will understand them. Technical terms are defined in the Glossary on page 47, for the benefit of parents and other helpers.

Assessment pages

The assessment pages may be used as an informal check on the child's achievements and include an assessment summary, which is presented in simple language and in a format that a teacher or parent can run through with the child.

A **Glossary and notes for parents** section is provided at the back of the book, on page 47.

Published by Schofield & Sims Ltd,
7 Mariner Court, Wakefield, West Yorkshire WF4 3FL, UK
Telephone 01484 607080
www.schofieldandsims.co.uk

Copyright © Schofield and Sims Ltd, 2010
Sixteenth impression 2021

Author: Carol Matchett
Carol Matchett has asserted her moral right under the Copyright, Designs and Patents Act, 1988, to be identified as the author of this work.

British Library Cataloguing in Publication Data
A catalogue record for this book is available from the British Library.

Editorial project management by Carolyn Richardson Publishing Services
Design by Oxford Designers & Illustrators
Printed in the UK by Page Bros (Norwich) Ltd

ISBN 978 07217 1145 4

Schofield&Sims

A Letters and Sounds resource

Sound Phonics

Phase Two

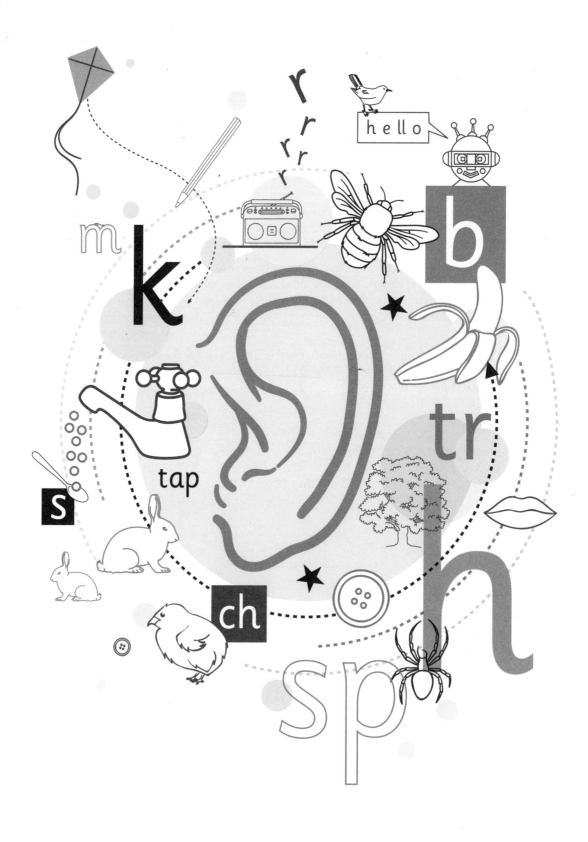

Name

The letter a

▶ Say the letter sound.

▶ Point to each letter and say the sound.

a a a

▶ Join the letter below to the things that begin with this sound.

The letter t

Say the letter sound.

t

Point to each letter and say the sound.

t   t   t

Join the letter below to the things that begin with this sound.

t

FOCUS ● recognise the letter **t** and say the sound that it represents
● select words that start with that sound

The letter p

▶ Say the letter sound.

p

▶ Point to each letter and say the sound.

p   p   p

▶ Join the letter below to the things that begin with this sound.

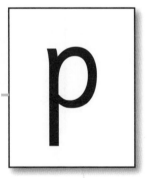

The letter i

Say the letter sound.

Point to each letter and say the sound.

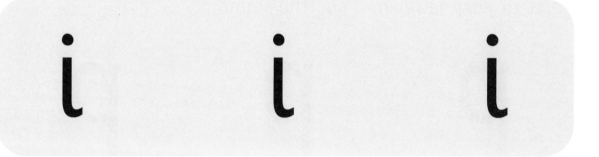

Draw a ring round each thing that begins with this sound.

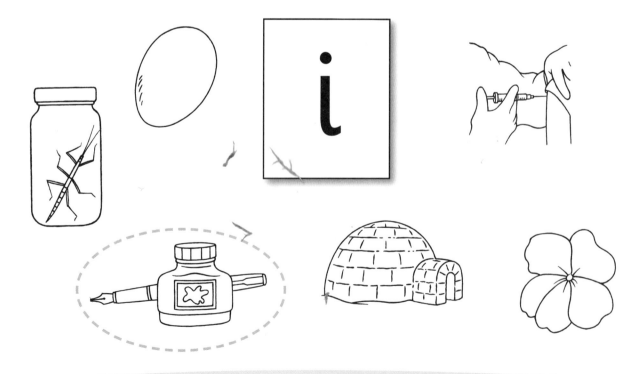

FOCUS ● recognise the letter i and say the sound that it represents
● select words that start with that sound

The letter **n**

Say the letter sound.

n

Point to each letter and say the sound.

n   n   n

Draw a ring round each thing that begins with this sound.

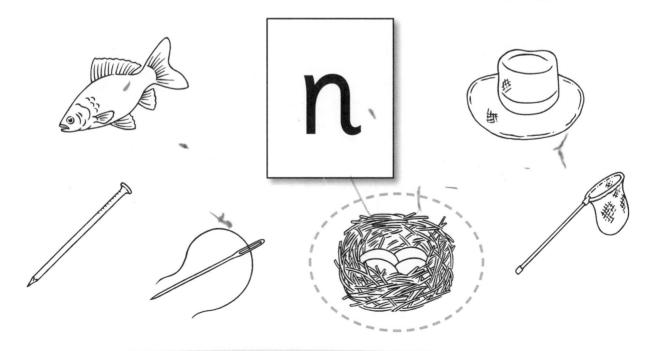

Blending for reading: Set 1 plus **i** and **n**

◗ Use **sound talk** to read these words.
Press the **sound button** as you say the letter sound.
Then **blend** the sounds to say the word.

◗ Colour the balloon when you can read the word.

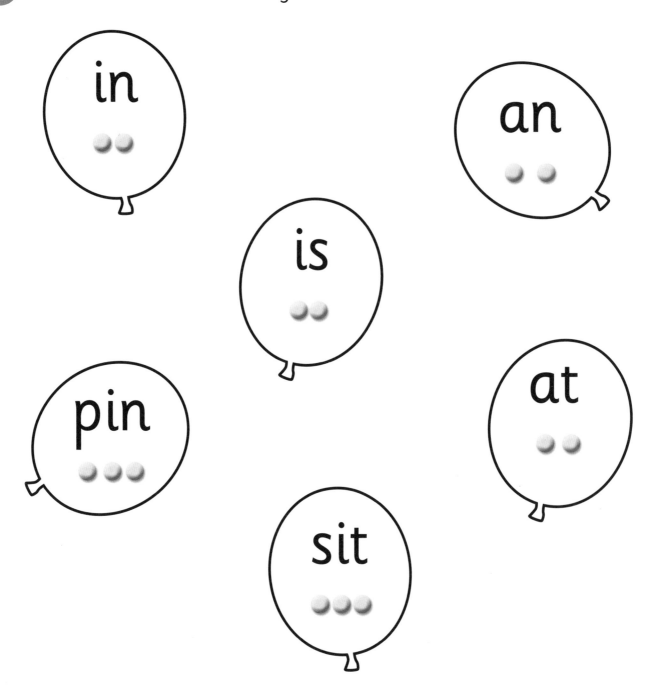

FOCUS ● recognise the letters **s, a, t, p, i** and **n**, and say the sounds associated with them
● understand that we say the letter sounds and blend them in order to read words (**blending for reading**)

The letter **m**

▶ Say the letter sound.

▶ Point to each letter and say the sound.

m　　m　　m

▶ Draw a ring round each thing that begins with this sound.

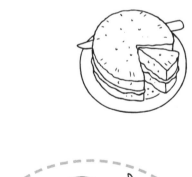

The letter **d**

◗ Say the letter sound.

d

◗ Point to each letter and say the sound.

d · · · d · · · d

◗ Draw a ring round each thing that begins with this sound.

FOCUS ● recognise the letter **d** and say the sound that it represents
● select words that start with that sound

Revision: Sets 1 and 2

Point to or trace each letter with your finger and say its sound.

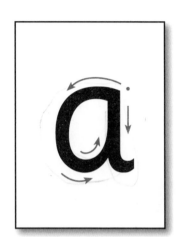

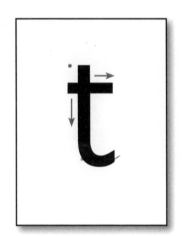
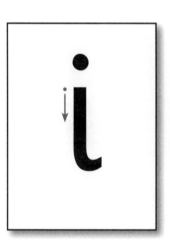

FOCUS   ● recognise the letters introduced so far and say the sounds associated with them
       ● recognise the letter that represents a given sound
       ● point to or trace letter shapes with one finger, as preparation for writing them

13

Blending for reading: Sets 1 and 2

▶ Use **sound talk** to read these words.
Press the **sound button** as you say the letter sound.
Then **blend** the sounds to say the word.

▶ Join each word to its picture.

man

mat

tap

tin

FOCUS ● recognise letters in words and say the sounds
● say and blend sounds in order to read words (**blending for reading**)

The letter **g**

▶ Say the letter sound.

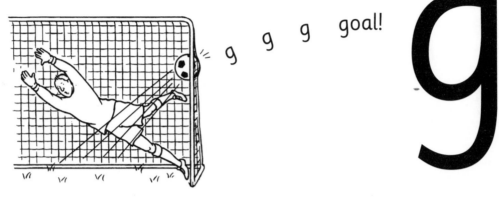

g g g   goal!

g

▶ Point to each letter and say the sound.

g   g   g

▶ Join the letter below to the things that begin with this sound.

g

The letter o

▶ Say the letter sound.

▶ Point to each letter and say the sound.

o   o   o

▶ Join the letter below to the things that begin with this sound.

FOCUS ● recognise the letter **o** and say the sound that it represents
● select words that start with that sound

Blending for reading: **g** and **o**

▶ Use **sound talk** to read the words on the balloons.
Press the **sound button** as you say the letter sound.
Then **blend** the sounds to say the word.

▶ Some of the words are real and some are made up.
Colour the balloon if the word on it is a real word.

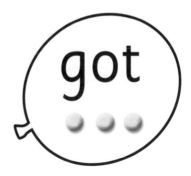

FOCUS ● recognise letters in words and say the sounds
● say and blend sounds in order to read words (**blending for reading**)

17

Segmenting for spelling: sound talk

Tog the robot speaks in **sound talk**.
He breaks up words into separate sounds.

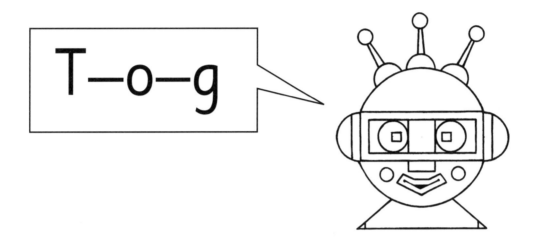

Help Tog to **sound talk** these words.
Draw a ring round the letter that Tog needs next.

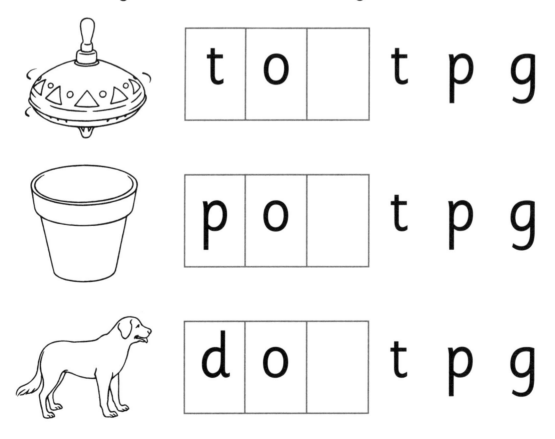

FOCUS ● understand that whole words can be **segmented** (broken up) into separate **phonemes** (sounds)
● select letters to represent those phonemes

The letter c

▶ Say the letter sound.

C

▶ Point to each letter and say the sound.

▶ Colour in the things that begin with this sound.

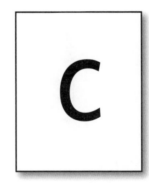

FOCUS ● recognise the letter **c** and say the sound that it represents
● select words that start with that sound

19

The letter k

▶ Say the letter sound.

▶ Point to each letter and say the sound.

k   k   k

▶ Colour in the things that begin with this sound.

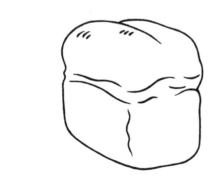

FOCUS ● recognise the letter k and say the sound that it represents
      ● select words that start with that sound

Revision: Sets 1 to 3

▶ Point to each letter with your finger and say its sound.

s a p t

i m n d

▶ Point to or trace each letter with your finger and say its sound.

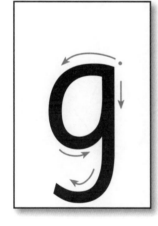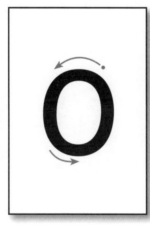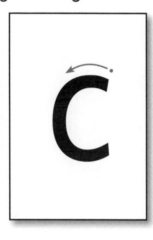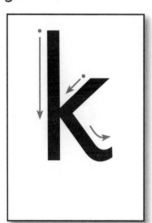

FOCUS ● recognise the letters introduced so far and say the sounds associated with them
● point to or trace letter shapes with one finger, as preparation for writing them

21

Blending for reading: **c** and **k**

▶ Use **sound talk** to read these words.
Press the **sound button** as you say the letter sound.
Then **blend** the sounds to say the word.

▶ Join each word to its picture.

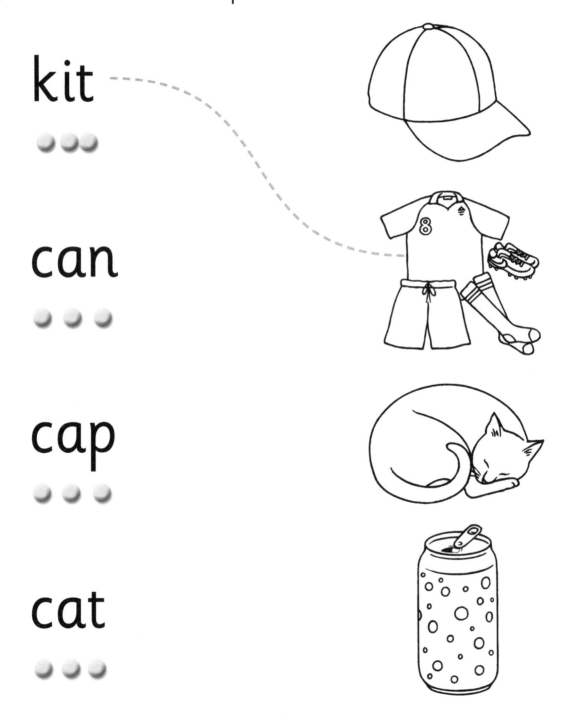

kit
● ● ●

can
● ● ●

cap
● ● ●

cat
● ● ●

FOCUS ● recognise letters in words and say the sounds
● say and blend sounds in order to read words (**blending for reading**)

Reading captions: **and**

▶ Use **sound talk** to read this word.
Press the **sound button** as you say the letter sound.
Then **blend** the sounds to say the word.

and

● ● ●

▶ Read these captions.
Use **sound talk** to read the words.
Join each caption to its picture.

dad and Kim

a cat and a dog

a man in a cap

FOCUS ● blend and read the **high-frequency** word **and** and recognise it in captions
● read captions by sounding and **blending** words

23

Segmenting for spelling: Sets 1 to 3

Remember, Tog the robot speaks in **sound talk**.
He breaks up words into separate sounds.

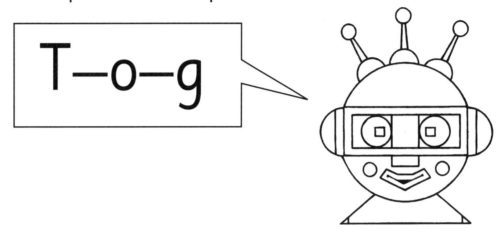

T–o–g

Help Tog to **sound talk** these words.
Draw a ring round the letter that Tog needs next.

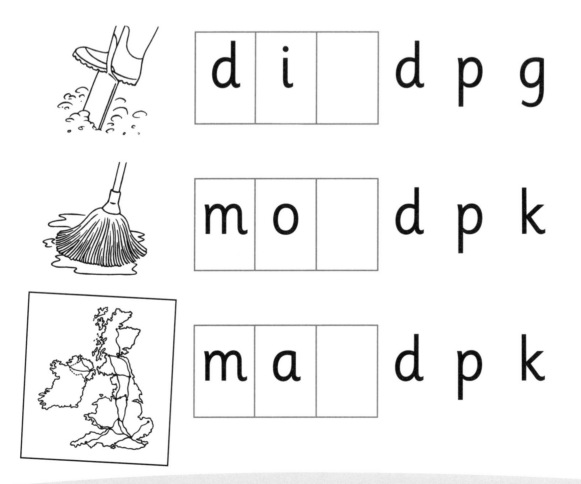

| d | i | | d | p | g |

| m | o | | d | p | k |

| m | a | | d | p | k |

FOCUS ● understand that whole words can be **segmented** into separate **phonemes**
● select letters to represent those phonemes

The letter **e**

▶ Say the letter sound.

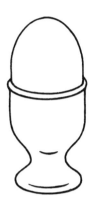

e

▶ Point to each letter and say the sound.

e   e   e

▶ Join the letter below to the things that begin with this sound.

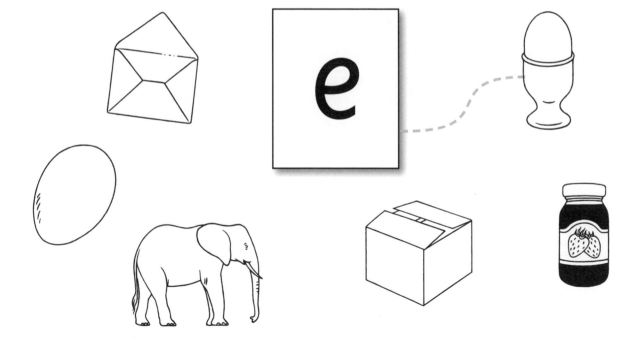

Blending for reading: *e*

Use **sound talk** to read these words.
Press the **sound button** as you say the letter sound.
Then **blend** the sounds to say the word.

Join each word to its picture.

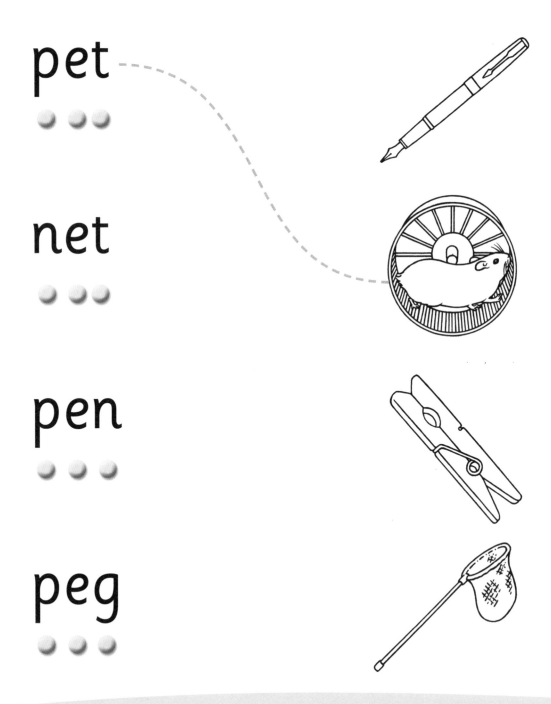

pet

net

pen

peg

FOCUS ● recognise the letter **e** in words
● say and blend sounds in order to read words (**blending for reading**)

The letter u

▶ Say the letter sound.

u

▶ Point to each letter and say the sound.

u   u   u

▶ Colour in the boxes that show the letter **u**.

| n | u | o |
| a | n | u |

FOCUS ● recognise the letter **u** and say the sound that it represents

The letter r

▶ Say the letter sound.

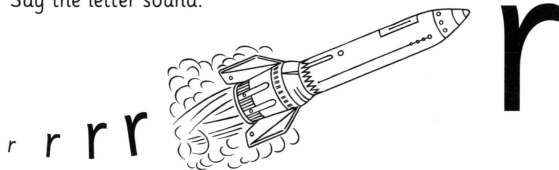

▶ Point to each letter and say the sound.

▶ Draw a ring round each thing that begins with this sound.

Blending for reading: Sets 1 to 4

▶ Use **sound talk** to read the three words on each line.
Press the **sound button** as you say the letter sound.
Then **blend** the sounds to say the word.

▶ Draw a ring round the word that goes with the picture.

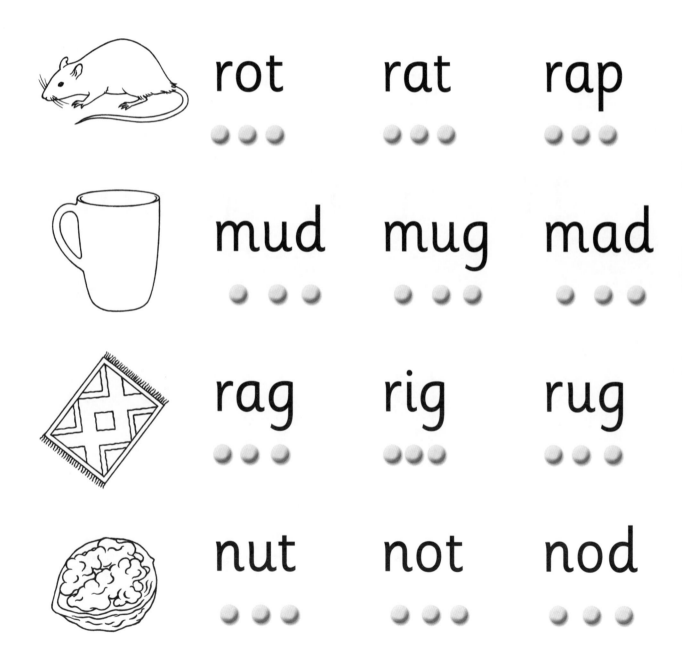

rot   rat   rap

mud   mug   mad

rag   rig   rug

nut   not   nod

FOCUS   ● say the sounds associated with letters
        ● blend the letter sounds in order to read words (**blending for reading**)

29

Segmenting for spelling: Set 4

Help Tog the robot to **sound talk** these words.
Draw a ring round the letter that Tog needs next.

| c | u | |

r p d

10

| t | e | |

n r p

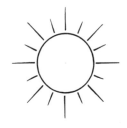

| s | u | |

r n m

| r | u | |

n g d

FOCUS ● **segment** words into separate **phonemes**
● select letters to represent those **phonemes**

Revision: Sets 1 to 4

Point to each letter with your finger and say its sound.

s t p a

i n m d

g o c k

Point to or trace each letter with your finger and say its sound.

FOCUS ● recognise the letters introduced so far and say the sounds associated with them
● point to or trace letter shapes with one finger, as preparation for writing them

31

Reading captions: tricky word **the**

▶ Read this **tricky word**.

the

▶ Read the captions.
Join each caption to its picture.

Sid the cat

Sid in the mud

Sid on the rug

Sid in the cot

FOCUS ● recognise the tricky word **the** and practise reading it in captions
● sound and **blend** other words in order to read captions

The letter h

▶ Say the letter sound.

▶ Point to each letter and say the sound.

h   h   h

▶ Colour in the things that begin with this sound.

The letter b

◗ Say the letter sound.

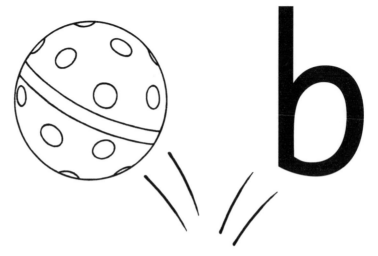

◗ Point to each letter and say the sound.

b   b   b

◗ Colour in the things that begin with this sound.

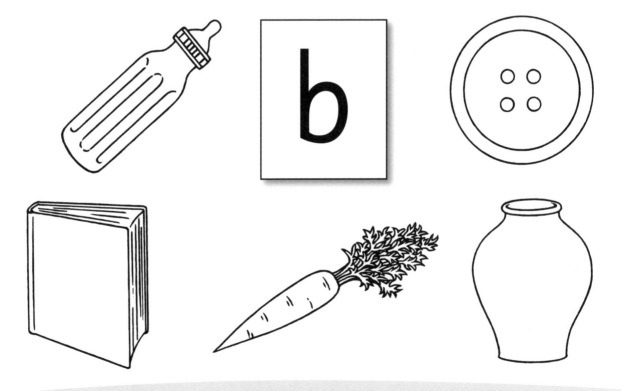

FOCUS   ● recognise the letter **b** and say the sound that it represents
● select words that start with that sound

Blending for reading: **h** and **b**

Use **sound talk** to read the three words on each line.
Press the **sound button** as you say the letter sound.
Then **blend** the sounds to say the word.

Draw a ring round the word that goes with the picture.

hot hat hap

bug bat bag

him hem hen

bus beg bun

FOCUS ● say the sounds associated with letters
● blend the letter sounds in order to read words (**blending for reading**)

35

Reading signs: tricky word **to**

Read this **tricky word**.
Press the **sound button** as you say the letter sound.
Look out for the tricky letter **o**.

to

Read the signs. Draw a line to show where each sign sends you.

to the top

to the bus

to the big cat

FOCUS ● recognise the tricky words **to** and **the**
● sound and **blend** other words in order to read simple signs

The letter **f**

▶ Say the letter sound.

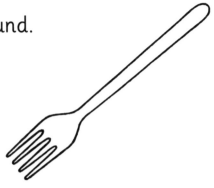

▶ Point to each letter and say the sound.

f   f   f

▶ Join the letter below to the things that begin with this sound.

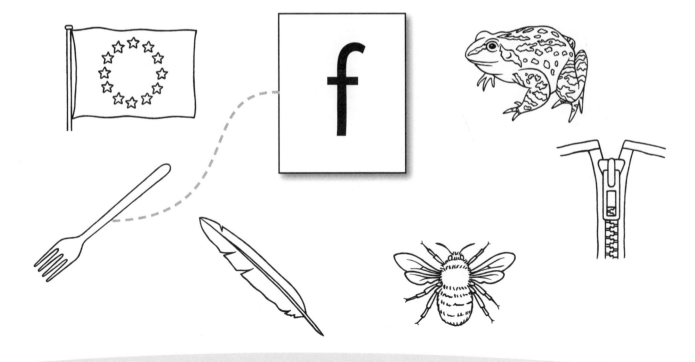

The letter l

Say the letter sound.

Point to each letter and say the sound.

l   l   l

Draw a ring round each thing that begins with this sound.

  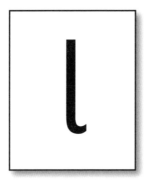 

FOCUS ● recognise the letter l and say the sound that it represents
     ● select words that start with that sound

Blending for reading: l and f

Use **sound talk** to read the words on the balloons.
Press the **sound button** as you say the letter sound.
Then **blend** the sounds to say the word.

Some of the words are real and some are made up.
Colour the balloon if the word on it is a real word.

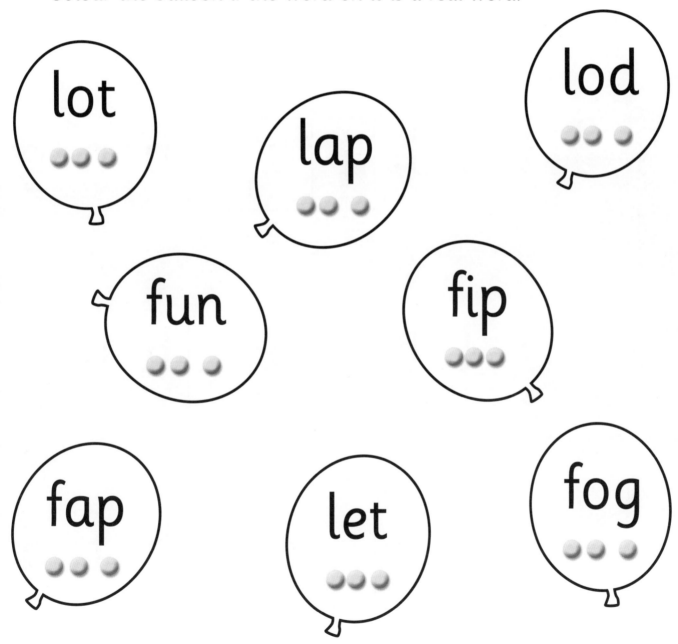

FOCUS ● say and blend sounds in order to read words (**blending for reading**)

Segmenting for spelling: **l and f**

Help Tog the robot to **sound talk** these words.
Draw rings round the letters that Tog needs.

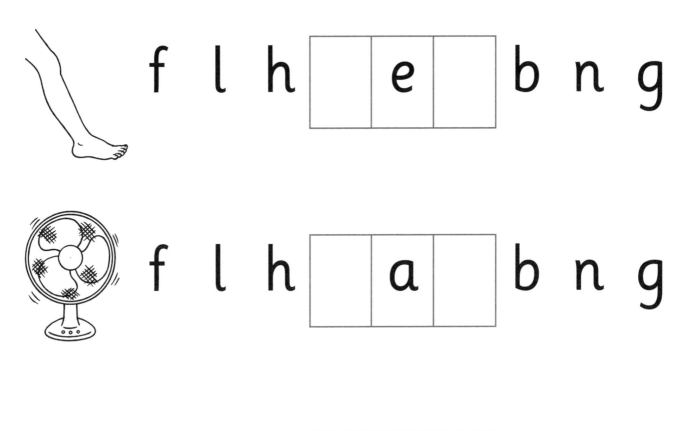

f l h | | e | | b n g

f l h | | a | | b n g

f l b | | u | | h n s

f l b | | u | | b t d

FOCUS ● **segment** words into separate **phonemes**
● select letters to represent those phonemes

Reading sentences: tricky word I

▶ Read this **tricky word**.

I

▶ Read each sentence.
Read the three words.
Choose the word that makes sense in the sentence.
Draw a ring round it.

I can _____ . hip hop hap

I can _____ . sat sit set

I can _____ . hum ham him

FOCUS ● recognise the tricky word **I**
● recognise the **high-frequency** word **can**
● sound and **blend** words for reading **(blending for reading)**

41

Reading captions: tricky word **no**

▶ Read this **tricky word**.
Press the **sound button** as you say the letter sound.
Look out for the tricky letter **o**.

no

▶ Pam has lost her hat. Read the captions and help her find it.

no hat in the bag

no hat on the peg

the hat is on Pam

▶ Draw the hat on Pam.

FOCUS • recognise the tricky words **no** and **the**
• recognise the **high-frequency** words **on**, **in** and **is**
• read captions, sounding and **blending** words where necessary

Reading notes: tricky word **go**

▶ Read this **tricky word**.
Press the **sound button** as you say the letter sound.
Look out for the tricky letter o.

go

▶ Read the notes. Join each note to its picture.

go to bed Sam

go to the log hut

let the bug go

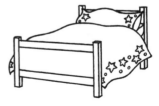

FOCUS • recognise the tricky words **go**, **to** and **the**
• read notes, sounding and **blending** other words where necessary

43

Assessment 1: letter sound check

Assessment 1 tests the child's knowledge of the letters and sounds introduced in this workbook. Check that the child can do the following.

1 Give the letter sound when you point to each letter.

2 Point to the letter when you say a letter sound.

s a t p

i n m d

g o c k

e u r

h b f l

Assessment 2: blending and segmenting check

1 Oral blending: say the letter sounds; ask the child to **blend** them to make the word.

rat	fog	nip	met	hug

2 Blending for reading: ask the child both to say the letter sounds and then blend them to make the word.

up	if	am	tan	din

3 Oral segmenting: point to each picture and say the word; ask the child to say the word in **sound talk** (like Tog the robot).

4 Segmenting for spelling: ask the child to help you spell four simple words (for example, **am**, **up**, **is** and **on**); say the word; ask the child to say the word in sound talk and then tell you what letters to write; write each word in one of the boxes below.

Assessment 3: tricky word check

Ask the child to read these **tricky words**.

the	to	I	no	go

Assessment statements

Run through with the child these assessment statements. Begin, 'Here is a list of the things you can do'.

I can say the sound made by any of the letters that I practised using this book. **(s a t p, i n m d, g o c k, e u r, h b f l)**	
I can point to any of these letters when given the sound. **(s a t p, i n m d, g o c k, e u r, h b f l)**	
If an adult says the sounds in a word, I can **blend** them to make the word. **(oral blending)**	
I can break down simple words into separate sounds. **(oral segmenting)**	
I can say and blend letter sounds to read simple words. **(blending for reading** of words such as **if, am, on, up)**	
I can use all that I know about letters and letter sounds to spell simple words. **(segmenting for spelling** of words such as **if, am, on, up)**	
I can read five tricky words. **(the, to, I, no, go)**	

What next?

You are now ready for **Sound Phonics Phase Three Book 1**.

Some children may not have fully grasped the skills of **blending** and **segmenting** but know all the letters; others may be unsure of a few letters, which you should keep practising together. Blending, segmenting and practising all the Phase Two letters continues in **Sound Phonics** Phase Three Book 1, so you can still progress to this book.

Glossary and notes for parents

blend	to say the separate sounds in a word and merge them together to make the whole word
	Blending is the reverse of **segmenting** and is an important skill to acquire when learning to read. **Oral blending** takes place when the child listens to someone saying the sounds and then blends them together to make the word. It is not necessary to have the word written down in order to do this. **Blending for reading** involves looking at a word, recognising the letters, saying the letter sounds and then blending them to read the word. This is more complex and at this stage many children will need help. Try saying the letter sounds aloud as you point to the letters. Then ask the child to say the whole word.
high-frequency words	common words frequently found in children's reading material and used by them in their own writing
	Children can read many **high-frequency words** by saying the letter sounds and blending them. By the end of Phase Two, most children can read in this way words like **it**, **is**, **him**, **but** and **big**. With practice, children start to recognise these words quickly and read them automatically – without having to say and **blend** the sounds. If your child recognises a word automatically, he or she no longer needs to continue using **sound talk** to read it.
phoneme	one of the separate sounds that a word contains
segment	to break a word into separate sounds in order to spell it
	Segmenting is the reverse of **blending** and is a skill that is vital to the process of learning to spell. **Oral segmenting** is breaking words orally into their separate sounds. The child does not need to identify the letters that make those sounds: the focus is simply on saying them. **Segmenting for spelling** involves breaking words up into separate sounds and choosing the letters that make those sounds in order to spell the word. At this stage, the child is not expected to write the letters or words: he or she needs simply to find and point to the letters.
sound button	a dot appearing below each letter, which the child presses as he or she says the letter sound; sound buttons encourage children to sound out each letter in a word in order to read it
sound talk	the process of saying, in the correct order, each separate **phoneme** in a word
tricky words	words with letters that make unusual or unfamiliar sounds
	The words **go** and **no** are **tricky words** because the letter **o** does not correspond to the sound that the children know for this letter. The word **the** is particularly tricky because none of the letters correspond to their familiar sounds. Children need to learn to recognise tricky words so they don't get stuck on them when reading.

Schofield & Sims

the long-established educational publisher specialising in maths, English and science

Sound Phonics prepares children for full fluency in reading, writing and spelling by providing intensive practice in phonics. A comprehensive phonics resource, it is fully compatible with *Letters and Sounds*, making it an ideal companion to this Government programme. **Sound Phonics** is equally suitable for use alongside any other incremental phonics teaching scheme.

The **Sound Phonics** activities, which are carefully graded and attractively illustrated, are best worked through with an adult. Right from the start they reinforce the child's early literacy skills through listening and speaking. From an early stage, the child is encouraged to look at and point to letters – and gradually to trace and form them correctly. He or she also practises identifying and saying the separate sounds in words ('segmenting for spelling') and blending these sounds to read words ('blending for reading'). Beginning with two- and three-letter words, the child slowly moves on to segmenting and blending longer words, including those with two or more parts. The child also practises reading and spelling 'tricky' words.

The first book in the series is a reusable stimulus book (**Sound Phonics Phase One**), which is designed for children in the Early Years Foundation Stage (EYFS). It is followed by nine one-per-child activity books for EYFS and Key Stage 1, which between them cover the developmental stages that *Letters and Sounds* refers to as Phases Two to Six. All the books in the series are listed at the foot of this page.

Each activity book supports teachers and other adult helpers by providing:

- integrated revision of points covered earlier
- 'Focus' statements, summarising the main objectives of every page
- assessment activities and an assessment summary
- explanatory notes
- a glossary of phonics terminology.

In **Sound Phonics Phase Two**, the second book in the series, the child practises letter Sets 1 to 5 and blends and segments short words. Responses to activities are made by circling, colouring or drawing lines. Pictures provide prompts for letter sounds and reinforce the child's growing recognition of letter shapes, which is further supported by finger-tracing. 'Sound buttons' help the child to say the separate sounds in a word before blending them for reading. Tog the robot encourages the child to use 'sound talk' when segmenting words for spelling – a technique that is used throughout the remainder of the series. 'Tricky' words are practised regularly from this point on.

Help every child to tune into literacy with this reliable and accessible series.

ISBN 978-07217-1145-4

GiftAid Donation

2663414197
WEST WICKHAM

For further in~~~~~~~~on and to place your order visit
www.schofieldandsims.co.uk or telephone 01484 607080

MIX
Paper from responsible sources
FSC® C023114

ISBN 978 07217 1145 4
EYFS & Key Stage 1
Age range 4–7 years

£3.95 (Retail price)